My AMAZING DIARY

London & Hertfordshire

Edited By Jenni Harrison

First published in Great Britain in 2019 by:

Young Writers
Remus House
Coltsfoot Drive
Peterborough
PE2 9BF
Telephone: 01733 890066
Website: www.youngwriters.co.uk

Foreword

Dear Reader,

You will never guess what I did today! Shall I tell you?
Some primary school pupils wrote some diary entries
and I got to read them, and they were **excellent!**

They wrote them in school and sent them to us here at Young
Writers. We'd given their teachers some bright and funky
worksheets to fill in, and some fun and fabulous (and free)
resources to help spark ideas and get inspiration flowing.

And it clearly worked because **WOW!!** I can't believe
the adventures I've been reading about. Real people,
make believe people, dogs and unicorns, even objects like
pencils all feature and these diaries all have one thing in
common – they are **jam-packed** with imagination!

We live and breathe creativity here at Young Writers – it
gives us life! We want to pass our love of the written word
onto the next generation and what better way to do that
than to celebrate their writing by publishing it in a book!

It sets their work free from homework books and
notepads and puts it where it deserves to be – **out in
the world!** Each awesome author in this book should
be **super proud** of themselves, and now they've got proof
of their imagination, their ideas and their creativity in
black and white, to look back on in years to come!

Now that I've read all these diaries, I've somehow got to
pick some winners! Oh my gosh it's going to be difficult to
choose, but I'm going to have **so much fun** doing it!

Bye!

Jenni

Contents

Jacob Carvill (7)   65

Hexton JMI School, Hexton

Thea Adeline Slater (6)   66
Finley Butts (7)   67

Mayville Primary School, Leytonstone

Shahza Usman (7)   68
Halima Asim (7)   70
Carolina Valentina Pacheco Rich (7)   72
Yusuf Lamin Jaiteh (7)   74
Amy Collis (7)   76
Zubeda Patel (5)   77
Erin Lily Smith (7)   78
Deluxshan Thayaruban (7)   80
Zain Kayani (6)   81
Benjamin Onasanya (6)   82
Reyhan Aktas (5)   83
Fatima Bilal (7)   84
Zuzanna Kacprzyk (7)   85
Shyanna Crosdale (7)   86
Alexandrina Kukurudza (7)   87
Emiliano Gjana (7)   88
Nana Osei Awuah-Baffour (7)   89
Karina Gabriluyk   90
Jasmine Rendall (6)   91
Isaiah Oshodi (7)   92
Junior James (7)   93
Andreas Apostol   94
Dina Tebani (6)   95
Yasmine Kerchich (6)   96
Faiza Mudhir (6)   97

Queensbridge Primary School, London

Arlo Jet Cadbury (7)   98
Bailey Graham (7)   100
Cassius Thompson (7)   101
Wendy Wang (7)   102

Zaafirah Rashaad Ogunfemi (7)   103
Jazlyn Moreno Becerra (7)   104
Jaylah-Jana Treasure Grant (7)   105

Randal Cremer Primary School, Hackney

Akorede Fathiu Oshikoya (7)   106
Tamanna Begum (8)   108
Cerys Castro (8)   110
Jamal Ssekilime (8)   112
Maisie Wallace (6)   113
Alfred-Daniel Akpey (8)   114
Ceyda Yilmaz (7)   115
Aaisha Jalilah Khanom (7)   116
Oghenevwede Akpioma-Martins (8)   117
Arda Akin (7)   118
Raynee Edwards (7)   119
Aniq Anir Ali (8)   120
Nelson Kumah (7)   121
Hatice Sara Gulsara Bilir (7)   122
Dina Sultan (7)   123
Billie-Rae Gooder (6)   124
Rihanat Salami (7)   125
Aisha Ali (6)   126
Mohamed Sharif Mohamed (7)   127
Kaydee Pinto (6)   128
Vinnie Butler (8)   129
Mark Anthony Barlow (7)   130

Shillington Lower School, Shillington

Toby Bishop (6)   131
Benjamin Dylan Shelmerdine (6)   132
Summer Olivia Loader (5)   134
Thea-Mar Greenwood-Mortelmans (6)   135
Martha Burr (6)   136
Limani Mauger (5)   137
Elliott Alexander Radelat (6)   138
Dexter Ritchie (6)   139
Adora Bella J Cordt (6)   140

Heath Kidd (5) 141
Lottie Howarth (5) 142
Chester Baker-Leach (6) 143
Teddy Witherspoon (5) 144
Leo Rome Scott (6) 145
Phoenix Williams (6) 146
Kai Barrett (5) 147
Elsie Daniel (5) 148

St Bernadette Catholic Primary School, London Colney

Bob O'Byrne Kehoe (7) 149
Anikó Coyne (7) 150
Alistair Nathan Hanna (7) 151
Noah Howard (6) 152
Holly Vanderhoven (7) 153
Megan De Sa Fernandes (7) 154
Chigozirim Okoh (7) 155
Maxwell Gatta (6) 156
Sienna Enstone (6) 157

Windermere Primary School, St Albans

Emily Sproule (7) 158
Ilia Bruce (7) 159
Idris Hylton (7) 160
Rose Fitzgerald (7) 161
Efehan Gok (6) 162
Sivani M Nair (6) 163
Safwan (7) 164
Scarlett Campbell (6) 165
Josh Treanor (7) 166
Tomos Hughes (7) 167
Mackenzie Stokes Boucher (7) 168
Darcie Bayliss (7) 169
Luke Winston Chapman (6) 170
Nailah Rahman (7) 171
Jayden De La Cruz (6) 172
Jake Lawrence Bishop (6) 173
Sophie Anne-Marie Hubbard (7) 174
Natanael Musija (7) 175
Hamzah Zaman (7) 176

Sol Cedillo-Cohen (7) 177
Ronin Marshall (7) 178
Taryn Marima (7) 179

Yewtree Primary School, Hemel Hempstead

Iaryna Andreea Tase (7) 180
Alyssa Steeden (7) 181
Lukas Rodière Davis (7) 182
Hafza Khan (6) 183
Maisie Puddephatt (7) 184
Oscar Harris (7) 185
Mason Stephen William Lane (7) 186
Marley-Jay Daniel O'Hara (6) 187
Saif Akthar (6) 188
Lola Rose Taylor (6) 189
Safa Akhtar (6) 190
Leo Atticus Trinder (6) 191
Sienna Wright (7) 192
Courtney Lawson (6) 193
Hira Khan (6) 194
Reece Keenan (6) 195
Cameron Thackeray (7) 196
Ollie Newton-Smith (6) 197
Dylan Thomas McLaughlin (6) 198
Freya Burch (7) 199
Riley Solomon (7) 200

The
Diaries

Dear Diary

Today has been the best day ever! I went to the funfair. We played games all day. I also went with my friend. We went there because my friend was surprising me for being her best friend for five years!
We went on the very fun Ferris wheel. My favourite part of it was the mega upper deck. It goes up then quickly goes back down. We loved it so much.
I saw loads of my other friends there.
I also played loads of games with them too! Such as teachers, the dog game, tag, stuck in the mud, infection and hello neighbour.
I also really wanted to be in charge of some of the games.
Me and my friends really enjoyed ourselves at the funfair. Oh yeah I forgot to tell you how we got there! We walked there. I hope this happens again!

Jochebed Adomah (7)
Cowley Hill School, Borehamwood

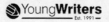

Dear Diary

Today I went to the park with my family because the weather was sunny and we played and had fun.
I went to the funfair to have fun and we went on lots of rides and there was a soft play and trampolines and walls for climbing and dodgems.
I went to play with my best friend and we had dinner and we watched a film.
I went swimming for a swimming lesson. I went for a horse ride because it was summer.
I went to the zoo and I fed the monkeys with bananas.
After school I went to computer games because my dad said so.
I went to gymnastics to practise. I went to football because I really wanted to go there.
I went to party because it was my birthday.

On holiday I went for a picnic with my
family.
I went for dancing because I had to practise
my dancing.
I went to lunch with all the children and I
sat next to them. At home I went upstairs in
my room and we played games with my
friend.

Galena Atanasova (7)

Cowley Hill School, Borehamwood

Dear Diary

Today I went to the funfair with a unicorn (Fluffy) and I met my cousin Arber. We went to get my picnic blanket and my sandwiches, carrots, ice cream, cake, cups, cupcakes, bread, Nutella and water. We went there because it was my birthday and I was excited.

When we ate the cake it was my fave part because the cake was covered with rainbow sprinkles, sugar powder, Nutella and it was vanilla flavour! My favourite flavour of cake. Then me and Arber played on the huge Ferris wheel, like really huge, huger than me, and when we got on it went really really fast and it stopped at the top!

Arber got scared but I calmed him down and then it started again. It stopped at

the bottom and we got out and went to the thing that goes up and down.
I hope this happens again.

Elsa Domi (7)
Cowley Hill School, Borehamwood

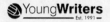

Dear Diary

Today I went to the park with Sonny and Kingston. It was a surprise for the summer holiday. We ate so much food. After we made slime together then we ate McDonald's at the park. Then we went to the Galleria and went to Sega, it was fun. The reason why I went is because I've been a good boy. We met a new friend.
The favourite part of the day was when we were playing Sega and got three prizes for us.
Then we came back to the park and I went into Sonny's car then came back home.
Then Kingston came to my house and it was another surprise.
Kingston had to leave at 9pm.
We played on my Nintendo Wii until it was 9pm. He said goodbye and I said goodbye.

The best moment was when we played Super Smash Bros. and when we picked the same character.

Gian Miguel Marcelino Padua (7)

Cowley Hill School, Borehamwood

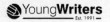

Dear Diary

Today I was so happy because I went to the zoo with my family. We saw monkeys, lions, tigers and elephants. After we had seen all the animals we went and got some ice cream.

Next we got on a truck and went to the hippos. We saw the hippos and one of them was in a lake. Oh I forgot to tell you, it was a sunny day and we all got an ice lolly! We went and saw the camels and we got on the truck again. It took so long! And the camels were asleep. It was so funny so then we went.

What did we miss to see? I know, zebras. We went and saw the zebras and it was so funny. Then we had a picnic. We had strawberries, bananas, ice lollies, water, watermelons and pears. After eating we went to the shops and I got a beautiful book about animals.

Maddie Mae Driver (6)

Cowley Hill School, Borehamwood

Dear Diary

Yesterday it was the best day of my life because I went to the funfair with my friend and we went on a scary dark ride that goes 99 metres high to a 100 metre drop. It was amazing, it was so fun.

It's my birthday. I've got a delicious cake, it's humongous. We have had a picnic but to my surprise my birthday cake has three layers.

After we had a barbecue and we had water slides out. We had a humungous one a high one a medium one and a small one and a bathtub for babies to try to swim. We also had a slushy area and a basketball court. We drew and sang and I played. Then I went to the movies, it was a long movie. I liked it because we had so much fun.

Kingston Laeon Joseph (6)
Cowley Hill School, Borehamwood

Dear Diary

We had the funniest day. We dug a hole in the ground and we found a secret tunnel and we met a magical fairy and also we went unicorn riding.
Next we went to have a picnic. After that we went swimming. My unicorn made the water float. It was so funny.
We played so many games. We ate loads and loads and loads of sweets.
Oh yeah and we found the house in the secret tunnel.
We went to a party, we were dancing. So much!
We went swimming with a mermaid and we had mermaid tails. We were in the sea so much, with my BFF Lillie Grace!
Then we went home and in the treasure chest there was a giant stack of sweets and they were really big.

Lacey Hunt (7)
Cowley Hill School, Borehamwood

Dear Diary

Today was so magical because I went with my BFFs and my cousins to Beano Town! It was so cool because we saw Mini the Minx and Dennis the Menace and we had a massive party with gymnastics and dancing. I found treasure when we wanted hot chocolate and loads of yummy sweets.
"We want more!" we shouted and we had more. It was great!
You should have been here because you would be able to find Roger the Dodger and he would be dodging someone like Walter. Then when you have passed Roger, you will see the Bash Street Kids.
It was so much fun for me and my friends. That was a great day but I have to finish. Bye!

Lila Mallinson (7)
Cowley Hill School, Borehamwood

Dear Diary

Today I went to the park with my family. I went to the park because it was sunny and it was a birthday surprise. We had a lovely picnic, we walked to the park because we wanted to enjoy sunshine. We nearly spent the whole day there. I saw lots of pretty and beautiful flowers, there were roses, daisies and others. I was so happy and excited. My dad and my mum went to buy some ice cream and I got chocolate ice cream with a flake. On the way to the park I saw my cousin Lea. It was so much fun. At the end we all had my birthday cake and it was chocolate, 'cause my favourite part was when I got to have my chocolate birthday cake.

Sara Saldumovic (7)
Cowley Hill School, Borehamwood

Dear Diary

Today I went swimming at the Venue. I always enjoy it when I go swimming. I went with my grandma. I had to go because it was my swimming lesson. I also went in the deep end and that's my favourite part. The deep end is about 1000 cm deep!

At the end of the lesson I met all my friends waiting for me to come and play with them. I was so surprised that they were waiting for me to play. We played it, hide-and-seek and Scrabble. We did a puzzle, stuck in the mud and teachers. It was the best day in the world! I was so lucky because my best friends came to my house for a sleepover at mine.

Olivia Staszewska (7)
Cowley Hill School, Borehamwood

Dear Diary

Today was a very weird day because I went to somewhere you would never go.
It all started when I was at school. It was home time. My mum let me and my friends go on a picnic. We went to a grassy place. Then we saw some things, they were Pokémon!
We followed them to a faraway land. They said we could keep them. We said okay.
Then we saw an evil T-rex but it tripped and fell in a volcano.
It went bubble, bubble, bubble, pop.
Then the volcano erupted, but the lava was too hot, it burnt the volcano down. Then the Pokémon led us back to our homes.

Josh Chesterton (7)
Cowley Hill School, Borehamwood

Dear Diary

It has been a crazy day. First, I met a real unicorn, I woke up at a unicorn land. I was so excited. Next, I had a unicorn ride and we made cloud angels. It was so fun.

After that, we had a picnic. We drank a magic milkshake. It was magic and yummy and we ate sweets and chocolates. Then, we played some games, gymnastics, art, dancing and we went swimming in the rainbow water.

We saw a mermaid. Then, we went to the unicorn house. It was so rainbow. We watched the movie of Lego 2, it was fun.

We met a fairy in the unicorn house.

Speak soon from Maria.

Maria Adanma Dike Baos (6)

Cowley Hill School, Borehamwood

Dear Diary

Yesterday I went to school to learn things and to write neatly.
I went with my granny. I went to the play park and I saw my friend and played with her and her sister.
I went to the zoo with my mum and dad because the sun came out and the big bus came for us.
I went to school with my friend with her dad because my mum and dad were at work.
I went to the funfair to have fun and it was good. I went to the train with my mum.
Yesterday I went to the park and I went with my granny and I played on the swing and the slide and I went on the roundabout.

Pandora Judit Daniel (6)
Cowley Hill School, Borehamwood

Dear Diary

Me, Max and Julia went to Red Land, we had a picnic party. We took our toy Pokémon. We drank smoothies and ate sweets.

We took a football, we played football for two hours.

Amazingly I found a hole. I started digging. Max and Julia saw me and asked me what I was doing.

I said, "I'm digging a hole."

They said they wanted to help!

I said, "Yes, you dig a hole and you dig on the other side."

They did. We put holes at the top. Around the mud we covered it with wood and holes. It was really fun. So so fun!

Daniel Lukaszewicz (7)

Cowley Hill School, Borehamwood

Dear Diary

Hi I'm a footballer. I am going to show some of my football skills.
1. Rainbow flicks.
2. Keepy Uppy.
3. Bicycle kick.
4. Kick.
Next, we played a football match. I scored twenty goals. Messi scored thirty. Then we had a lunch break.
Finally I won. I scored forty goals and Messi scored twenty. We are the champions! We are the Champions of the World!
We talked about football all the time and again and again and again. We finally had a break from talking about football all of the time.

Daniel Fox (7)
Cowley Hill School, Borehamwood

Dear Diary

Today I went to see a unicorn at a farm. I got to ride the unicorn but it did not fly.
I had a picnic with the unicorn, I had a strawberry milkshake, a cucumber, a ham bagel, a pack of salt and vinegar Hula Hoops, a jam mini roll and a pack of yummy chocolate. I ate it all and messed up my top. I got an extra milkshake for the unicorn. She already drank eight of them except the ninth one because she spilt it down herself. The unicorn was so full she then went to sleep on her rainbow.
I had fun with a unicorn.

Esme Isabella Sheehan (6)
Cowley Hill School, Borehamwood

Dear Diary

Today I went to a football pitch with a football player, let's just say Messi.
I played football, I played computer games and I played races. It was fun playing with Messi.
When we were playing we came to a sparkling treasure. Next to the sparkling treasure there was a Pokémon! A Pokémon, isn't that amazing?
It was so fun until there was a tiger. Isn't that scary? I don't know. But he just wanted to play with me and Messi.
I wonder what will happen tomorrow?

Oscar Przepiora (7)
Cowley Hill School, Borehamwood

Dear Diary

Today I went to the park with my mum, dad and baby brother because it was a sunny day. I stayed there all day to play. We took some food to eat when we were hungry. For food we had potatoes, banana, water and orange juice. I played football with my friends. I rode my scooter through the park. We got the car to go to the park. We had big big fun. We were hungry so we started eating. My favourite part was scooter riding because I like it. I saw my friend Jonoton. I hope it happens next year.

Patrick Andrei Sava (6)
Cowley Hill School, Borehamwood

Dear Diary

I was playing a computer game outside when I saw this gold light. It was coming from a pile of rocks. I moved them out of the way. When I cleared away the rocks, it was a secret tunnel.
I decided to go through it. I saw my gang and Power Rangers.
Me and my gang gasped. They showed us around.
Suddenly Josh showed up. He gasped. Josh said, "Is that the Power Rangers?"
Me and the others said, "Yes!"
Josh gasped.

Gerard O'Sullivan (7)
Cowley Hill School, Borehamwood

Dear Diary

This was the coolest day that I have had in my life. It all started when I was looking for my slime on the beach.

After that we found my slime. But we found it in a secret tunnel and found gold, emeralds, diamonds and iron.

That was in a safe vault. We took all of the things that were in the vault. We took them home and we played Minecraft. Me and Rishan, Danif, Dan L, Josh, Bengi, Gerard and Alfie.

We had a party.

Andrew Yannis Hramov (7)
Cowley Hill School, Borehamwood

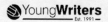
Dear Diary

Today I went to the funfair with my friends and with my friends I played football then we had a picnic. My mum let me because it was my birthday. It was really fun, so fun and my favourite ride was the Ferris wheel and the roller coaster. Then we went to go to get something to eat, like chocolate bars and some ice cream. We had lots of fun with my friends. It was really nice.

Sonny O'Neill (7)
Cowley Hill School, Borehamwood

Dear Diary

Today I went to the beach with my family and we found treasure. Firstly it was very sunny.
Next I saw a jellyfish, crab, starfish and turtles in the water. After that I had a picnic. We had jam sandwiches and for dessert I had ice cream. Next we got a shovel and dug a massive whole.
Finally we got home and relaxed and got all snuggled up and watched a family movie.

Reggie Smith (6)
Cowley Hill School, Borehamwood

Dear Diary

I went to the park to play and I saw Kojo and played football today. Yesterday I went to a party. Then I went to a computer games day. In the evening I went to play in the garden. And today I went to the zoo and played. I went to the zoo with Kojo and Victor and Stanley. My favourite was the park and the zoo because I saw Kojo.

Marcel Marfo (6)
Cowley Hill School, Borehamwood

Dear Diary

Today I caught Pikachu at a Pokémon funfair and I went on rides with Pikachu. We did that because it was Pikachu's birthday party. That's why we went in the first place. When we were there we got a cake for Pikachu. And we had toys for Pikachu! My favourite part of the day was eating Pikachu's birthday cake.

Oliver August (6)

Cowley Hill School, Borehamwood

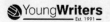
Dear Diary

Today I went to the park and saw my friends Emi, Madie and Siana. We had lots of fantastic fun. It was so lucky that my family said you can go on the assault course. It was also sand. I got to see my cousin and I had a lovely day with my family. And I went to a cafe and I had a milkshake.

Olanike Rachael Olateru-Olagbegi (6)
Cowley Hill School, Borehamwood

Dear Diary

Today I went to the park with my family. I played with my friends at the park and we played games at the park til 10am.
We ate ice cream then we ate food then I played hide-and-seek. Then I went on the swing, then on the slide and then I played football.

Ciprian Costin (7)
Cowley Hill School, Borehamwood

Dear Diary

I went to the funfair with my family and I saw treasure. I went to a secret tunnel and then I drank milkshake and my dad bought me a Pokémon.
I played football and I was dancing and I ate lunch and I ate chips. I played games and I did art.

Benjamin Fuat (6)
Cowley Hill School, Borehamwood

Dear Diary

I went to the park with my friends. We found art and a fairy. I ended up dancing with Mia and Casey C.
I felt happy and excited and my friend ate sweets.

George Irvin (7)
Cowley Hill School, Borehamwood

Dear Diary

Today I went to LegoLand with my whole family. It was the hottest day of summer. When we went through the entrance, we saw crowds of people queuing up for the rides. I queued up for the spinning spider ride with my cousins.

One hour later, we finally got on the ride. Suddenly, the huge plastic spider from the ride began to crawl.

"I'm hungry!" he roared.

Thousands of mini spiders roamed around everyone's feet. People screamed and tried to escape. But the huge spider shot sticky webs at the entrance and exit gates. Now everyone was stuck.

At that moment, a plan popped into my head. Spiders hate water, so we needed to take the spiders to the Viking River Splash ride. Trying to be brave, I dashed to the river and shouted for everyone to follow me. The spiders crawled after us.

Everyone jumped onto the ride and the spiders fell into the river with a huge *splash!* I had saved the day.

Maryam Imran (6)
Date Palm Primary School, London

Dear Diary

I went to Alton Towers with my family and some of my cousins on 6th September 2018. We went for a holiday and we stayed in a hotel named Premier Inn. We went by minibus and it took nearly five hours to get there.

At Alton Towers, we followed a map to find the ride that we wanted to go on. First, we went to CBeebies Land, where we climbed up a tree and went on a ride so we could see the whole of CBeebies Land.

After that, we went to some more ride like The Postman Pat Van, Go Jetters ride and the roller coaster ride. Then we saw Nina's Science Lab and a Bing show. We played mini golf and bowling which we enjoyed so much. Then we had lunch under a massive tree.

After lunch, we went to a pirate boat and played with water cannons. Then we came back home at night-time.

I really enjoyed my holiday in Alton Towers and I want to go there again when I can go on the fire roller coaster and spend more time.

Irfan Raza (6)
Date Palm Primary School, London

Dear Diary

Today was an amazing day! I jumped out of bed to get to the airport for our holiday in Dubai. I hurriedly got my bag ready and packed it with colouring and my iPad.
When me and my family were ready, we got into the big, black taxi. We passed the richest place in England, it was Buckingham Palace. I saw the Queen's guards wearing black, fuzzy helmets. They looked hilarious! We finally arrived at the airport, gave our suitcases and boarded the plane. I felt excited and a bit nervous. Luckily, I sat next to the window.
The plane ride was rocky and all of a sudden, the plane flew to space. I couldn't believe my eyes. There was a blue, ten-eyed monster. It was a friendly monster and it waved at me. At last, we arrived in Dubai. See you later!

Muhammad-Isa Hussain (7)

Date Palm Primary School, London

Dear Diary

On Sunday, I went to Epping Forest for a walk with my club. We went by the top speed train and when we were on the top speed train, we saw the Queen Mary line, it was the fastest train in town. The train's colour was blue then we got off after four stops.

When we were walking in the forest, we saw five or seven horses and we saw other people that were there and it was a farm. I got tired after walking a little bit. Then we saw a frog on a rock. The other people in the club went on a scary adventure in Epping Forest and we got to eat our lunch. When we finished, we got to play in the park. When it was home time, the club teacher gave us all stickers. Then we went home on the train again.

Mohammed Hamzah Bin Miah

Date Palm Primary School, London

Dear Diary

My favourite holiday was to Antalya on 20th October 2017. I went with my mum's extended family, there were 42 of us in total. We all had a blast. We stayed at a luxurious resort, there were four swimming pools and a games room that we played in every day.

I experienced quad-biking for the first time, I rode with my mum. She was the fastest and the best driver. It was a thrilling experience! We also visited some beautiful beaches and mountains, we ate some delicious food and ice cream. The weather was perfect, the sun was out but there was a nice breeze. It was so special to spend a week with my family. I was sad to leave the amazing views and the lovely weather.

Maisarah Bint-Akthar (7)
Date Palm Primary School, London

Dear Diary

I went to a huge forest. I saw a big dolphin. His name was Jack. Jack was a nice dolphin so he didn't want to eat people but one day, he saw someone that he didn't know. He tried to eat him up but he could not eat him. The thing was a shark. The shark didn't know him either so they both told each other their names.

Then the dolphin came to the shark's house. They became friends. They went to a swimming pool. The shark leapt out of the water and landed on the dolphin. The dolphin did it too. They did it until night-time.

They snuck out and went under the bed. Then they started sleeping but woke up to a big noise...

Sabina Tayeb Boudali (6)
Date Palm Primary School, London

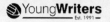

Dear Diary

I woke up today and I was thinking how my day would go. I went to the bathroom and brushed my teeth, thinking of how to make my day fun because I didn't want another boring day like Saturday. After that, I had breakfast and made a plan on a piece of paper.

I showed it to my mum, she said, "We can go to the farm today."

I was so excited that I couldn't wait to go! I looked out of the window, it looked cloudy. When we got ready, we left as soon as possible. When we got there, we got to do some arts and crafts and looked at the animals. When we left, I felt really happy.

Zaynab Risvegli (6)

Date Palm Primary School, London

Dear Diary

I went to the funfair with my family. We went on a Saturday because it was a family fun day. I went there because it was a special occasion. I used a car to get there. I played on the horses and I had bubblegum-flavoured candyfloss. I went on a bumper car, it was very fun. We all had ice cream and lots of treats.

I also saw my friends, then I got on a ride with them. It started to get dark so I went to my house.

As I was going into my house, my friends shouted, "Thanks for today! We had a really nice time."

Ilyas Mohammed (7)
Date Palm Primary School, London

Dear Diary

Today has been an excellent day at school. I went to Pizza Express with my class to learn how to make pizza.

Firstly, we took the DLR train to get there. On the train, I played I spy with my friends, it was so much fun.

Then at Pizza Express, we made and decorated our own pizza. We all got a chef's hat to wear. My hat had the number one on it. When we finished, we took a double-decker bus back to school.

Lastly, at the end of the day, I took my pizza home to share with my family. It was delicious!

Zakariyya Abdul Wadud
Date Palm Primary School, London

Dear Diary

One hot, sunny day, we decided to go to Victoria Park. We went to the park by bus. From the last bus stop, we had to walk for a while to get to the play area within the park.

In the park, we played with the slides, swings and bridges. Then we fed the ducks. It was so much fun! There were so many trees and small lakes. We also ate snacks while playing. We played football too and when we finished playing, we stopped on top of the bridge and watched a boat go past and then took a bus back home.

Zainab Malik (6)

Date Palm Primary School, London

Dear Diary

I went to an exciting family fun day. There were balloons and food and cakes. It was amazing and surprising. I went with my brother, my cousins and my auntie. We all played together. I liked the jumping area. I went on Saturday, it was a sunny day. I went because it was fun and cool. My brother made a painting which said 'Musa' in Arabic. We walked to the family fun day, the walk was beautiful.

Isa Ahmed
Date Palm Primary School, London

Dear Diary

I went to Sainsbury's to buy toothpaste. Then I went for a long walk with my parents. After that, I went to the park and played for a tiny bit. Then I went to my fascinating friend Nuha's house. We played together. Her mum served us very tasty food. Finally, I went back home and used the toilet, washed my face with hot water, brushed my teeth and straight away went to bed.

Sabirah Rawdah Sanaullah (6)
Date Palm Primary School, London

Dear Diary

I went to the museum with my family. I went on the 1st March. I saw a Water-type Pokémon. I saw a dinosaur skeleton. I looked at the old toys in the museum. I saw a monster next to me. The monster showed me a make-and-do centre.
Later, it was time to go so I said bye to the monster and that was the end.

Ibrahim Mohammed Abdullah (7)
Date Palm Primary School, London

Dear Diary

One amazing, hot day, I went to the amazing funfair. I saw a little unicorn. After, I was lost so I went on the unicorn. The unicorn had powers so then I went on it. I went home.
I said to the unicorn, "Come back please, come back next time. Please, please!"
Then the unicorn went.

Caaisha Ahmed (7)
Date Palm Primary School, London

Dear Diary

I went to the library. I went with my family on 10th March 2019 to read good books. I got there on the train. I made slime. I did art and I played. We had a party and we played games. We had lunch, we went swimming, we saw a mermaid. We had sweets and smoothies. We read good books.

Maryam Mohammed Abdullah
Date Palm Primary School, London

Dear Diary

First, when I woke up, my brother did too. I used the toilet and then I brushed my teeth. Then I went downstairs to play and my dad came downstairs too. Then my mum made breakfast. Then I went to play at my aunty's house for the day.

Dawud Abdul-Mukith (7)

Date Palm Primary School, London

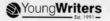
Dear Diary

Saturday: My sister went to my grandmother's house. Me, my brother and my mum went to my nani's house. Me and my brother and cousin played together.

Sunday: We were stuck at home. We watched a lot of TV today.

Rahma Mostafa
Date Palm Primary School, London

Dear Diary

Today, I went to the funfair with my family.
Me and Benyamin went on the cars and the
trampoline and the roller coaster. We
bought candyfloss and lollies. My cousins
were already there. We had lots and lots of
fun.

Sue'ad Nazrana (6)

Date Palm Primary School, London

Dear Diary

Last summer, I went to London Zoo with my family. I was so excited the night before the day I was planning to go to the zoo. We reached the zoo at eleven o'clock in the morning.

First, we went to the aquarium. I was eagerly waiting to see the shark. The fact is, there was no shark. Then we went to Gorilla Kingdom. We saw a shy, scared gorilla sitting in the cage. Also, we took pictures and I saw a very funny monkey's red bottom. After that, we went to see the tigers. I wanted to hear the tigers roar but they were too grumpy. So, I couldn't hear them at all.

So then, we saw a big, furry camel, white llamas, fat muddy pigs, pink flamingoes standing on one leg and a family of goats. After our lunch break, we went to see the king of the jungle. Same as the tiger, the lion was grumpy and also sleepy.

Our next move was to see the penguins. They were very good at swimming. They dived into the pool, jumped out and back-flipped in the pool again. The funniest part of this trip was the giraffes. I saw her long neck. There was a food bucket next to an empty bucket, so the giraffe with her long neck and tongue, got the bucket and ate all the food.

Next to the giraffe cage, we heard ferocious sounds coming from it. We saw lots of hyenas were howling in their cage. Now, then it was time to leave, we were thinking about the elephants. We were looking for it but we couldn't find it anywhere. Then a zookeeper told us that there was no elephant at the zoo. I was so disappointed and sad. After that, we went back home and rested.

Mahveen Sayed (6)

George Tomlinson Primary School, Leytonstone

Dear Diary

At the weekend, I visited the trampoline centre at Walthamstow Leisure Centre. I went there with my mum and cousins and my aunt. We took the 257 and 97 buses. When we arrived, I got so excited and straight away, I wanted to go inside but I needed to wait in the queue at the till. I had lunch with my cousins, Dylan and Liam. I had to wear special sticky socks and a wristband before they let me in. When I entered, I saw some big, soft blocks and I jumped into it and pretended to swim. After, I balanced and climbed on equipment. I was jumping a lot on the trampolines.

I played tag with Dylan, then I went to the play area with him. There was a football cage on the floor so I took a ball and scored a goal. Then I wanted to go to the slides. It was like a secret tunnel but I was not scared and I went down but it was curvy and long and dark.

There was a place there that looked like a forest and I went there with my cousins and suddenly, my mum jumped out, pretending to be a bear with a roar! We ran away as fast as we could, the bear started to chase us. We got very tired and wanted to have a rest, a glass of water and a delicious snack at the hall. I had so much fun and it was the best day so far.

Armand Horvath (7)

George Tomlinson Primary School, Leytonstone

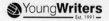

Dear Diary

Today is Saturday. It's the weekend and we're always busy as we have so much to do. Today, we had to go food shopping and we didn't like going to Sainsbury's. But we had to go. I helped with the bags and no surprise, Aaria is too lazy to help. Mummy and Daddy put everything away. Then we got ready to go on our bikes, that was so much fun and we fed the ducks.

After, we went to Pizza Express for lunch and then we joined in with a quiz in WH Smith. We had to guess how many coins were in the jar. I guessed 200 and Aaria guessed 80 but I knew I was closer. Then we chose our books to buy. I chose 'Five Minute Stories'. We had to leave because we had to go to our swimming lessons. It was so much fun as they were doing a challenge in the pool. We had to swim in a square and a teacher gave us coloured bands when we passed her. I got 32 bands and Aaria got 11. My legs were tired.

Then we had a sandwich for dinner, I read my book and fell asleep.

Kirika Hothi (7)

George Tomlinson Primary School, Leytonstone

Dear Diary

On Tuesday, I went with the GT Dance group to the Borough Dance Showcase. This was held at another school called Hillyfield Park. We had to travel by bus to get there. We had been practising our dance routine for the past ten days and we all felt confident in our moves. While watching the other schools' performers, I felt nervous but also excited to get on stage.

Once it was our turn, I put my nerves behind me and focused on remembering the routine. I thought we did a brilliant job and we all enjoyed ourselves. The only thing to spoil our day was getting soaked in the pouring rain on the journey back to school.

Suhayla Ismail (7)

George Tomlinson Primary School, Leytonstone

Dear Diary

One day before Christmas, I went to Winter Wonderland with my family. I saw different games and an icy castle. Then we got inside and saw different kinds of ice statues. But my favourite statue was a princess. Inside, the icy castle was too cold because otherwise, the statues could be melted. Then in the icy castle, we took pictures of us. After the castle, we saw a circus but it was closed. After all the fun, we were very hungry so we took a hot dog and it was very yummy.

Karina Korotii (6)
George Tomlinson Primary School, Leytonstone

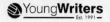

Dear Diary

On Saturday, I went to space with a green, slimy monster. The monster had three eyes! I went to space with a monster because it was lost so I took it home to see his mum and dad. I bounced on the moon with the monster's family. Then I ate some cheese pizza from my spaceship and I had some moon cake. I felt very happy because it was fun!

When I went home, I said goodbye to the monsters. I said I would come back soon and I did come back to see the monsters.

Isobel Jones (7)
George Tomlinson Primary School, Leytonstone

Dear Diary

Today, I went to a theme park called Adventure Island with my family. It is located at the beach side of Southend-on-Sea. I took various rides like Green-Scream, The Cow Jumped Over The Moon, Barnstormer, etc. But my favourite ride was Skateboard. I also enjoyed playing at the indoor soft play. I had sugar doughnuts, waffles and candyfloss. I went on the giant wheel and I saw pebbles on the beach. I enjoyed there so much that I want to go there every month.

Darsh Agarwal (6)
George Tomlinson Primary School, Leytonstone

YoungWriters
Est. 1991

Dear Diary

Today, I went to Rainbowland. I slid down a rainbow with my unicorn friend, Sparkle. Sparkle is seven and I am six.
I made a rainbow and it was fun. I met other unicorns too. Then we saw Sparkle's mum and dad. We went to Sparkle's house and had dinner. Then we went to sleep and dreamt about the next day.
The next morning, we went to a fair and then we went to a party and we had fun. Then I went home.

Kiera Flinter (6)
George Tomlinson Primary School, Leytonstone

Dear Diary

I did science with a friend called Venes and we made a smoothie. When we were finished, we showed it to the class and our teacher, Mrs Chantel, was happy for us. Venes wrote a diary and she felt so proud. Venes brought it to class and Sharan felt jealous. Everyone likes Venes' diary.

Jedidiahan Damptey (7)
George Tomlinson Primary School, Leytonstone

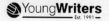

Dear Diary

Today, I went to the barbers with my dad and sister. We went there to shave my dad's hair. I went on a bus to get there. On the way, we saw a lot of shops. At the barbers, there were plenty of fish in an aquarium. I saw orange fish and light orange fish and they ate orange cubes.

Edwin Kwaku Daniels (6)
George Tomlinson Primary School, Leytonstone

Dear Diary

Today, I went to a beach called Zlatni Rat with my family. It had waves as big as a tree! If you tried to walk, you would be blown back to the sandy shore. When I tried to walk, my goggles fell off! I was jumping the waves and I tried to swim.

Jacob Carvill (7)
George Tomlinson Primary School, Leytonstone

Dear Diary

Yesterday I went to a cave with my best friend Darcey. Firstly we found an alleyway full of crystals. Then we found a secret tunnel. At the end of the tunnel we found a... huge red dragon! The dragon was asleep. After that we tiptoed out and suddenly the dragon woke up and blew fire! We ran out of the cave and hid. Next the dragon stopped. We went near it and it looked really sad. So me and Darcey said, "What is the matter?"
It said, "I have lost my baby!"
So we helped. Meanwhile we found it. The big red dragon was so happy. Finally we went home. We said to each other, "That was so fun!"

Thea Adeline Slater (6)

Hexton JMI School, Hexton

Dear Diary

I went to the park with my family. I brought my football too. I went climbing. First I climbed all the way up. Then I played football. I scored lots of goals, it was fun today.
There was an ice cream van. I had a mint one.

Finley Butts (7)

Hexton JMI School, Hexton

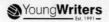

Dear Diary

I went to school on Monday and learnt about division in maths. I went to school on Tuesday and had spellings and tests. I went to school on Wednesday and had PE and recorder. I went to school on Thursday and went to assembly. I went to school on Friday and did the register and went to assembly.

On Saturday, I woke up in the morning slowly because I was still sleeping but I was hungry too. I went downstairs to have breakfast. I ate it quickly because I was excited about the evening because I was going to my auntie's house. While we were waiting, me and my sister and my mum, Misha, played hide-and-seek.

When me and Misha were done, we were incredibly tired but then we heard our mum say it was time to get ready. I wondered because it was not evening, it was morning.

My mum said, "Because it is far and we are always late, we are going early this time and we are getting ready early."
We were on time but one thing, my auntie was late!

Shahza Usman (7)

Mayville Primary School, Leytonstone

Dear Diary

I went to a fairy house with my pink, pretty and precious unicorn because I love unicorns and fairies. Also, I was dancing and having lots of fun because I was having a party with my beautiful and lovely unicorn. I even love dancing but I wanted to go horse riding then we went horse riding and I was extremely excited but I was also scared. So I just said, "Can you help me?"

So she said, "Okay, I will stop," and I said, "Thank you."

Next, I went on holiday with my fairy and my unicorn. I was going because who would look after them? I had to go with them. I do love them and we were going to dance there. Sometimes, we were not going to dance but sometimes we did and we were going to dance now. Then we were not going to dance and I was going to go back, even my fairy and my happy unicorn were going back and we loved our holiday.

Now we are sleeping because we are tired.

Halima Asim (7)
Mayville Primary School, Leytonstone

Dear Diary

I was sleeping in my warm, pink bed when I heard a noise but I thought that I was just dreaming so I went back to sleep. I heard it again so I went to look out of the window and I saw a unicorn, I named her Tracy. She was so colourful when I saw her, she was only five years old. Now, she's ten.

One day, we were eating lunch when we heard a noise coming from the house next door so I jumped on her and we rushed next door. We were about to open the red door when we saw a shadow. It looked like a monster and that's when me and Tracy found a green, hairy monster but we also found out that he was harmless. He just wanted a friend to play with and then me and Tracy took him home.

Then a magical experience happened, the monster was changed into a whole family and that family was our family of unicorn and humans. They were fantastic.

Carolina Valentina Pacheco Rich (7)
Mayville Primary School, Leytonstone

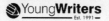

Dear Diary

Today, I went to Wakanda and met Black Panther, King and Protector of Wakanda. I always wanted to meet him on Challenge Day when they battle and fight. I was watching him and Black Panther won the battle. All of the brave Wakandans were very happy with him. Then they buried him so he could see his father.

After that, he showed me around Wakanda. Then Killmonger went to Wakanda from America while Black Panther was sitting on his shiny, beautiful throne. Killmonger went in the palace and he started arguing and said that he wanted to have a challenge with T'Challa. So on another Challenge Day, when I was watching them, T'Challa got beaten up and he lost. Killmonger threw T'Challa down the waterfall and his mother and sister were shocked.

Killmonger said he was king and he had the necklace and Wakanda was beaten.

Yusuf Lamin Jaiteh (7)

Mayville Primary School, Leytonstone

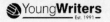

Dear Diary

Today, I walked to the forest to see the wild animals. Suddenly, I stepped on something unusual. It felt like a bird egg, as I took my foot off of it, slime burst out at me. I was shocked! The slime led me to a unicorn city. I was just walking, looking around the place and then I fell down a secret tunnel. I walked to see more but then I saw a man holding up a sign saying: *Welcome To Thailand.*

I said to myself, "I'm probably in a different country, that was definitely a secret tunnel!"

I went to explore and surprisingly, I fell down another tunnel. It, luckily, led me to the unicorn city. I went to search for the first tunnel but it had disappeared. I shouted, "No!" as I was stuck in the unicorn city!

Amy Collis (7)
Mayville Primary School, Leytonstone

Dear Diary

I am Zubeda Patel. My family is my mum, Aisha; my dad, Makbul; brother, Mohammed; and sister, Sumaiya. My school is Mayville. I am Year 1, class three. My little sister is at the same school, in the nursery. I play with my sister. I have two friends in my school, I play all the time with them. I read my school book every day and do my homework. Sometimes, me and my sister watch cartoons. I love eating food and fruit, I drink orange juice. I love going shopping with my family. I love to go on holiday. I go to my aunty's house and to parties and I love birthday parties. I love dancing. At home, I can help my family. I help tidy up and I love to help my brother because my brother doesn't talk.

Zubeda Patel (5)
Mayville Primary School, Leytonstone

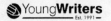

Dear Diary

On Friday, me and Fatima went to the swimming pool and splashed about in the water. Then we dried our bodies and went in my room and played with a doll.

On Saturday, I went to the zoo with Jasmine and my mum. We looked at the animals.

On Sunday, we went to the funfair. I went with my friend, Yusra, and we went on a roller coaster and got some candy.

On Monday, it was my birthday and my mummy and daddy took me to my birthday party and we had great fun.

On Tuesday, me and Alex played Minecraft and watched Minecraft.

On Wednesday, I spent time with my teacher, family and friend and ate loads of unhealthy food.

On Thursday, I played with all my friends.

Erin Lily Smith (7)

Mayville Primary School, Leytonstone

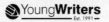

Dear Diary

I am seven years old. I had my friends at my birthday party. I had a 'Power Rangers' cake on Saturday 9th February 2019. I had some party balloons and I had plates, cups, cards and presents. My dad, my mum and my friends took pictures and I played with my toys while my mum and dad opened the presents. I got a toy motorbike and some dinosaur toys. My mum put music on and I was dancing with my friends then my mum and dad were dancing with us. I ate milk chocolate, it's my favourite. I was finding treasure, it shows money on the treasure map.

Deluxshan Thayaruban (7)
Mayville Primary School, Leytonstone

Dear Diary

I had a beautiful day. I went to school and after school, I thought about going to another school because at school, it was crazy hard. So I went and saw the school and saw the children were not bossy and they were beautiful and not loud. There was a lot of work to do because the children were reading at the park and some were doing their work. But when I was going up, it was getting harder and harder but I will try my best to get past the years because I want to get past school, high school, university and work because I want to be free and rest.

Zain Kayani (6)

Mayville Primary School, Leytonstone

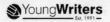
Dear Diary

I was in the park with my mum and my dad and my brother. We were flying our kite and our frisbee and our ball and everything was so nice. Dad was playing football and frisbee and he helped us to do our kites. When it was night-time, we went home. We ate dinner then we put our pyjamas on and we were watching 'Om Nom Stories' for the whole time. I love 'Om Nom' because it has good stuff in it, it doesn't have bad things. Then I went to sleep for the whole night.

Benjamin Onasanya (6)
Mayville Primary School, Leytonstone

Dear Diary

I went to the park and I got an ice cream. It was chocolate flavour, I loved it. I went on the swing, it was so fast that I fell down on the floor. I was bleeding a lot but I was not crying at all even though it was still hurting. After that, I ate a cake, it was so yummy and great.

After that, I went to the trampoline park and I was playing hide-and-seek. I was the winner, the prize was to choose where we were going next and I chose McDonald's. I got a toy.

Reyhan Aktas (5)

Mayville Primary School, Leytonstone

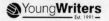

Dear Diary

Tuesday 19th March, 2019
Today, I needed to go to bed because it was my bedtime so I changed into my fluffy PJs. Then I went to bed and I had this weird dream. I was in a horse place, I mean I was in a horse pen, and I saw this gorgeous unicorn. I went up to it and it was adorable! It loved me and I said, "I will take her!"
I had a horse pen and I called her Lucy.

Fatima Bilal (7)
Mayville Primary School, Leytonstone

Dear Diary

I went with a white and black talking rabbit to the Barbie life in the doll's house then I went with a green and furry monster to the water park. I splashed the monster quickly! I went to school with a pink and fluffy unicorn, we played with the trays full of blue water and we went to the play gym. I went with my family to the zoo, we saw a monkey. It bit my cousin's finger!

Zuzanna Kacprzyk (7)
Mayville Primary School, Leytonstone

Dear Diary

I went to a park then I played on the slide and then I went on the swing. I saw an alien come into the park. I screamed and then another came. I screamed as loud as I could and then I left the park. I went to the funfair and got an ice cream. Then I saw an alien again. I ran as fast as I could but then he came for me. I went home and he followed me there.

Shyanna Crosdale (7)
Mayville Primary School, Leytonstone

Dear Diary

I was sleeping at night and in the morning. I went on holiday with my unicorn. When I was walking with my unicorn, I saw a beautiful dress in the shops and it cost 101 pounds and I didn't have money left.
100 days later, I still didn't buy it, yet one more day later, I finally had enough money. All £101 and I bought it.

Alexandrina Kukurudza (7)
Mayville Primary School, Leytonstone

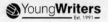
Dear Diary

This morning was a freshening morning. I was getting ready to go to the zoo. I dressed up to go to the zoo, I was ready and I went with my family. I was in the car and I was excited to go. First, I saw the monkey. After, I saw the parrots, elephants, giraffe and the lions. I had a fantastic time at the zoo.

Emiliano Gjana (7)
Mayville Primary School, Leytonstone

Dear Diary

I went to my friend's house. Me and my friend walked to the skate park. First, I went on small jumps, then big jumps. Then I did so many ramps. I did it with my bike. There were so many people. Me and my friend played basketball in the basketball court. I played basketball, I got 100 dunks and 50 shots.

Nana Osei Awuah-Baffour (7)

Mayville Primary School, Leytonstone

Dear Diary

My family is my mum, Tanya; my dad, Misha; and I, Karina. We often like to walk. Once, we went to the park, we had lots of fun together. We took a picnic with us: candy, vegetables, chocolate and we drank milkshakes. Dad played with my bodyball. We loved playing different games. We are a friendly family.

Karina Gabriluyk
Mayville Primary School, Leytonstone

Dear Diary

Today, when I went to school with my friends, I had lots of fun. At school, I have three golds, five silvers and five bronze. I work hard no matter what and I really want a headteacher award! Because everyone else laughs at me and I don't like it.

Jasmine Rendall (6)
Mayville Primary School, Leytonstone

Dear Diary

I would read books every day and I never stop reading as books make your brain smarter. It helps you get good concentration and when you get better, you can read to babies and babies will understand people. I love reading, Diary.

Isaiah Oshodi (7)
Mayville Primary School, Leytonstone

Dear Diary

Yesterday, I went to London Zoo. It was very fun because I saw a lot of animals. The monkeys were jumping up and down. I saw a huge gorilla sleeping on the hammock. The giraffes had long necks and purple tongues.

Junior James (7)
Mayville Primary School, Leytonstone

Dear Diary

I played football with the monster in the park. It was so fun and we played with the ball. I was so excited and we ran and played games and I was happy. It was the best day ever.

Andreas Apostol
Mayville Primary School, Leytonstone

Dear Diary

Today, I was playing in the garden with my brother and my cat called Ginger Cat. I played on the trampoline with my brother and my cat. We all had a wonderful day at home.

Dina Tebani (6)

Mayville Primary School, Leytonstone

Dear Diary

I went to the park. It's been so much fun and I went to the slide and my sister went on the swings. It's been the best day and I love to play there.

Yasmine Kerchich (6)

Mayville Primary School, Leytonstone

Dear Diary

I went to my gran's house and my dad took me to McDonald's and I had a milkshake and an ice cream and a Happy Meal.

Faiza Mudhir (6)

Mayville Primary School, Leytonstone

Dear Diary

I'm an alien student in a huge school made of a strange metal. The metal is from an old space station. I am in a crisis - can you help me?

Five days later...

Today I started school so me and my mum creaked open the rusty metal door and stretched our long legs and quietly walked into the metal corridor. Suddenly, a strange-looking figure came smartly walking down the mountain of steel. She was wearing a white space outfit. My mum said she must be an astronaut. Soon after, a tsunami of children came like cheetahs. I followed them until we got to an amazing, shiny, glistening, sparkly corridor. We sat down in neat little rows. I can up to the front and introduced myself.

Two weeks later...
Now I've made some friends and I've got one best friend.

Arlo Jet Cadbury (7)
Queensbridge Primary School, London

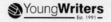

Dear Diary

Today was the best day ever. Let me tell you my day: I slouched to the park that morning. I climbed up to the monkey bars and staring at me was a fairy! Just then, I remembered that it was a school day. The fairy looked lonely.
"Would you like to come with me?" I said. She shouted yes and I carried her in my hand to school.
At school, I was worried that the teacher would confiscate her so I kept her a secret. She loved art but we also did spellings, maths, literacy and finally, at the end of the day, we had science. Then I had to take her home. When we were at home, we had to say goodbye. I was very upset when she left Goodbye Diary.

Bailey Graham (7)
Queensbridge Primary School, London

Dear Diary

In the jungle, a monster crashed down three trees. It had eyes as bright as the moon. Trees have been smashed everywhere in the adventure. Lots of things were rebuilt so nothing was wrecked. They have got flaming rocks and all he did was hit them back. Nothing was good. He opened his gigantic mouth and gobbled everything! Lots of knights failed badly. His teeth were as sharp as swords, his scales were as strong as shields and nails were as sharp as spears.

But there was a knight who was the best fighter and was as good as heaven and he slayed the monster's head and took it for a trophy.

Cassius Thompson (7)
Queensbridge Primary School, London

Dear Diary

Today, I went to the fantastic funfair. It had an amazing view: colourful fairy lights, bumpy bumper cars. Fairy Wendy suddenly popped up and said that she could come to join me on the roller coaster. It was very scary and fun at the same time. Then we went to buy ice creams. I bought an orange ice lolly. It was yummy. It started to get cold so I went into the indoor arcade. When it started to get dark, I went home, back into my cosy bed and fell asleep before my head hit the pillow and that was the end of my day.

Wendy Wang (7)
Queensbridge Primary School, London

Dear Diary

Today is the worst day, my mum has died. It all started when a horrible, nasty witch in the disguise of a slave gave my mum food and poisoned her. Let me tell you the story... In the morning, my mum had breakfast in bed. She had poison in her drink then she left. So now I have an evil mum and I think that's her! So now, I'm trapped and she's really rude. She hurt my friend and she threw me in a dungeon. Now, I must go, bye.

Zaafirah Rashaad Ogunfemi (7)

Queensbridge Primary School, London

Dear Diary

In the morning, I went to my grandparents' house and I saw my cousin. After a while, we went to the park and we had a picnic but there was a funfair. Then me and my cousin went to the funfair and had some fun. After an hour, it was time to eat. I was so hungry. At ten o'clock, me and my cousin said goodbye to my grandparents. After a minute, me and my sister went to bed.

Jazlyn Moreno Becerra (7)
Queensbridge Primary School, London

Dear Diary

I had a great weekend. I was with my little sister. My daddy bought us a puppy and a L.O.L. doll. We had a family party and I played with my sister and my cousins. We had nice food and chocolate cake and an Easter egg. I had so much fun with my lovely family. I love my amazing family.

Jaylah-Jana Treasure Grant (7)
Queensbridge Primary School, London

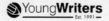
Dear Diary

Today was the worst day ever. This morning,
I went to school and it was fun because we
were learning about Romeo and Juliet. We
started to write and then we went to lunch,
Just as the clock struck five o'clock, smoke
and fire came out of houses. I was feeling
scared and petrified and I didn't want my
house to be burned because I would not
have any food and I might starve to death.
While I was thinking, I went to PE.
It was now hometime. My parents never
picked me up.
"They usually pick me up," I said to myself,
so I had to go home with a strict teacher.
She was strict to me for no reason. We go
to her house quick and I had to clean
everywhere, the fire got worse and worse. I
felt shocked and sad. Next, there were
flames running into homes and burning
them. It was really sad and I was sad and
scared something could happen to me.

I could have got burnt in the fire and it could have been the worst day ever.
I hated this day, it was a day I would surely not forget. It was not fun. I felt angry because the teacher was treating me badly. The village was almost destroyed. It was a sad story for me and my parents. *I wish today was a good day*, I said in my mind. There were lots of volcanic eruptions happening. This is definitely the worst day ever.

Akorede Fathiu Oshikoya (7)
Randal Cremer Primary School, Hackney

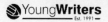

Dear Diary

Today was a horrible day. It was 8am in the morning, a sunny day and I was off to school. As I was walking to my class, I saw everybody looking out of the windows. I was looking out the window and saw smoke. I thought it was from someone's house. It was a sunny day. I ate food and went to playtime. I came back to class and it was shaking.

I was looking out of the window again and saw more smoke. I also saw bricks falling down on the floor. I was feeling scared and tired. The smoke was like fog. This was after lunchtime, at 1pm, everything was shaking. But never mind, let's move on. We started handwriting and spelling for an hour which took us to two o'clock. Then after we had to do PE for about twenty minutes, then we played something. This time it took us to three o'clock.

At three o'clock, I looked out the window again and saw more smoke. I also saw dark smoke and because there was dark smoke, I knew something dangerous was going to happen. I saw a house on fire.

It was time to go home. Going home took me one hour. Then I was here, eating my packed lunch because I didn't finish it. Then it was 5pm in the evening. I looked outside, there was more fire. The houses were on fire. There was more and more smoke. Many people died.

Tamanna Begum (8)

Randal Cremer Primary School, Hackney

Dear Diary

It was 4000BC. We didn't know how all the prey was getting out. The day we were getting prey, we saw something extraordinary... A hawk, something that nobody has seen before. We ran and told our father.

He said, "A hawk, that's not good."

He said that because it would eat our farm shop and animals.

A few years later, we saw people coming with this weapon, we were dying to know what it was. The people told us that they were called the Beaker people and they discovered bronze. We loved it. But a few hours later, war started. We went to a person who said we couldn't create war between ourselves. I woke up and there was war. It didn't look pleasant. We were horrified but the future-seer stopped it immediately. They lived in hillforts to protect them from the attack by the red knights.

The war barely happened again and that's what happened in 4000BC.
But the war wasn't ended. For the time, we still hated each other and faked it to the seer. We fought for our lives, for the children, also for our god, we fought for life.

Cerys Castro (8)
Randal Cremer Primary School, Hackney

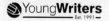

Dear Diary

Today was a crazy, fun day. I woke up, then I took a walk around the woods and then I found a cave full of cave paintings. I named it that because it was in a cave and it looked like paint. I ran back home to spread the word. Later that day, my dad said that we needed to have a feast. What I didn't like was I had to hunt the animal.
Years later, I was mining through rocks then I found something called bronze. I wish I found it first because the guy, Zeph Zeph Williams, lived in a rich house made out of bronze. At least we made weapons out of it. I always wondered if there were any more materials out there. You never know.
Then there I was searching for different materials, mining for hours, days and weeks and then I found iron.

Jamal Ssekilime (8)
Randal Cremer Primary School, Hackney

Dear Diary

1st November, 1911

I left Cape Evans with my team this morning, all five of us set off on our journey. They brought a lot of food and water to survive and they also brought tablets, a tent, ponies, dogs and a motor sledge to use. The weather was snowy, cold, windy, wet and soggy. I was feeling very excited but at the same time, I was scared because the Norwegians might get there before us and we didn't want that. I was feeling very cold, I should have brought something to warm me up.

20th December, 1911

I've been in Antarctica for a month now. I need to have a rest but I just can't let the team not be the first one to get to Antarctica.

Maisie Wallace (6)

Randal Cremer Primary School, Hackney

Dear Diary

Today was fun and weird, but it was more fun than weird. So me and my family went to Chessington to have some fun. So we first went to the Sea Life Centre and after, we went to go have lunch. Then we were going to the scorpion ride. While we waited in the queue. there was this person who put their hand in and there was a scorpion. On the ride, there was fire and the big robot scorpion squirted water on us! After the ride, we went to Tiger Rock and when we were on the boat, we kept on going up and up until we finally reached the top and splashed back down. Then, because of Peter, we went on the Gruffalo ride and we all had a water fight. Then it was time to go.

Alfred-Daniel Akpey (8)
Randal Cremer Primary School, Hackney

Dear Diary

Today, I went inside my imagination somehow. I saw my imaginary friend who I'd known since I was two years old. She told me that I was inside my head. I thought to myself, *how is that possible?* Then I decided I should have fun so everywhere was candy. I decided to have a treat, literally for an hour. Then I went to the best shop, the slime shop. I bought every type of slime you could ever imagine. I nearly got the whole shop! Then I felt hungry so I went to Taco Bell. Then I went to an Italian ice cream shop! After, I was really full but sleepy, so I stayed in my imaginary friend's house and that was the end of my day.

Ceyda Yilmaz (7)

Randal Cremer Primary School, Hackney

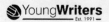

Dear Diary

Today, I time travelled to the Stone Age which was a long time ago, there was stone everywhere. Then I went to hunt animals. Later, I shot my first animal, I was so happy. Afterwards, I did cave paintings with my family.

The next day, some people called Beakers came and told us about bronze. Everyone who was around me was so shocked. Afterwards, little kids were digging for bronze and copper.

Two days later, people called Celts came and told us about iron. We had lots of enemies so we had to tell a Druid if we wanted to fight. We had hillforts so we could see for miles away. It was the best day ever!

Aaisha Jalilah Khanom (7)
Randal Cremer Primary School, Hackney

Dear Diary

You wouldn't believe what happened when I was at school. The building started shaking, we thought that it was an earthquake! Suddenly, we started to see smoke, we were running around madly. After a while, I discovered that it was getting worse, rocks were coming out of the volcano. I felt like I was going to have a heart attack or faint. I quickly ran to other classes to see what they were doing and rushed back to my class. I zoomed home and saw my mum packing.

She said, "We're moving to France."

I was so happy that we were going to survive.

Oghenevwede Akpioma-Martins (8)

Randal Cremer Primary School, Hackney

Dear Diary

It was amazing. I saw the Stone Age time. I woke up in the Stone Age, I was confused about how I got there. When I woke up, the bed was made of rocks, it was uncomfortable but I was fast asleep. The next day, they found bronze and I knew the Bronze Age had begun. I played with the other children, it was fun. I had my own home, then a person came. I didn't know who it was, he gave me some soup. The next day, I was tired. I now explored and it was the Iron Age. I didn't know what to do. I went to sleep and I was back home.

Arda Akin (7)

Randal Cremer Primary School, Hackney

Dear Diary

My name is Raynee and today, I saw a creepy doll. She said to me, "Hello, my name is Merry."

Merry was creepy, she went to the park soft play and even to parties. So I decided to throw her out the window but she came back. I tried everything but she came back every time. She was so annoying.

Suddenly, an old lady appeared in my bedroom.

She said, "Have you tried everything?"

I said yes. The old lady said to buy a unicorn and I said okay. I bought a unicorn and the doll went away.

Raynee Edwards (7)

Randal Cremer Primary School, Hackney

Dear Diary

I had a great day! First, I got ready to go to the park with my brother, Abir. Next, I went to the park and saw my friend, Kobe. Then I saw his sister but after 21 minutes, she was gone. Then I played with Kobe and we played our game named Hero X. In that game, we were heroes and we saved the day. But then, my friend fell down and got hurt really bad. He had to go home but his sister came again and played. We played dodgeball and it was fun! Then we played Simon Says. Finally, we went home.

Aniq Anir Ali (8)

Randal Cremer Primary School, Hackney

Dear Diary

29th March, 1912

We are all exhausted and extremely tired. The weather is freezing cold, it is soggy and wet. There is a terrible blizzard, it is as cold as ice. We won't make it home. The best bit is we finally reached Antarctica. The worst bit is we are short on food. We will stick it out until the end, but we are getting weaker, of course. The end cannot be far. It seems a pity but I cannot write anymore.

Nelson Kumah (7)

Randal Cremer Primary School, Hackney

Dear Diary

1st November, 1911
I left Cape Evans with my team this morning. Five of us in total. All of us put our packs on a sledge. I brought food, healthy vegetables and gooey fruits. We brought motor sledges. They were so, so fast. It was cool. Healthy chocolate bars and medical kits. I felt excited and wanted to be the first to go. The weather was bad at the South Pole. It was so, so cold in the South Pole.

Hatice Sara Gulsara Bilir (7)
Randal Cremer Primary School, Hackney

Dear Diary

29th March, 1912

We were so tired, I could not walk because the weather was freezing cold. We all heard the blizzard. I thought we couldn't get home now. At first, the journey was great because the views were amazing but now, I had the worst pain. We shall stick it out to the end but we are getting weaker, of course! The end cannot be far. It seems a pity but I do not think I can write anymore.

Dina Sultan (7)

Randal Cremer Primary School, Hackney

Dear Diary

Yesterday, I took my unicorn to school. Then I had tea with my unicorn and I had playtime with my unicorn. I went to bed with my unicorn.

The next day, I brought my unicorn again and my friends came and touched it. "That is furry and fluffy," they said.

I played with my friends and my unicorn.

Billie-Rae Gooder (6)
Randal Cremer Primary School, Hackney

Dear Diary

I left Cape Evans this afternoon with my team of five men. My team and I put all our luggage on a motor sledge. Our ponies carried the motor sledges with the help of the dogs. The weather was terrible. We packed a lot of healthy food. The ice was so thick with white snow. I felt enthusiastic and excited.

Rihanat Salami (7)
Randal Cremer Primary School, Hackney

Dear Diary

I left from Cape Evans. Five of us in total. I packed enough food with equipment and supplies, medical bags and also, sweets. We jumped on the ship. We decided who was steering, we're off. Let's check how far we are from Antarctica. Quite far...

Aisha Ali (6)

Randal Cremer Primary School, Hackney

Dear Diary

1st November, 1911

I left Cape Evans, excited. I brought lots of food and medical kits. I brought ponies and motor sledges to carry all the supplies. The weather was okay but really cold. We had to go through the ice to win the race.

Mohamed Sharif Mohamed (7)

Randal Cremer Primary School, Hackney

Dear Diary

20th December, 1911
Today, there was a blizzard. We left the pony behind. I was very tired. The weather was cold, we finally reached the South Pole. We felt sad, we felt disappointed. We used a balloon as excitement.

Kaydee Pinto (6)
Randal Cremer Primary School, Hackney

Dear Diary

One day, I went to McDonald's to buy six chicken nuggets and a medium-sized milkshake with large chips. I know you think I'm crazy but I also bought everything on the menu including a Big Mac.

Vinnie Butler (8)
Randal Cremer Primary School, Hackney

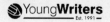

Dear Diary

When we left camp, I put my slippers on. The five of us had frostbite. The weather was freezing cold, it was night-time and we went to sleep.

Mark Anthony Barlow (7)
Randal Cremer Primary School, Hackney

Dear Diary

Today I went to Pokémon World with my pet Pokémon, Absol. We went on a plane and on the way, we saw a black Gliscor. Soon after, we landed at the Pokémon world. Then we started running out of the plane. Then we saw an Ultra Wormhole opened. We decided to enter the Ultra Wormhole, so I needed to use my Pokémon Garchomp who is a flying shark Pokémon. I jumped onto Garchomp's back and I went flying on his back so fast. Soon after, we landed at the Ultra Beasts' world and we saw lots of people there. Then we decided to leave the Ultra Wormhole. Then I caught a Pikachu. Then I went to the sea and I had a ride on a Sharpedo.

Toby Bishop (6)
Shillington Lower School, Shillington

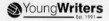

Dear Diary

Today I went to Sweetieland and I went with ten aliens. There I saw sweets and cabbage and I saw the Sweetie King. I also saw the King of Conker Sweets and I was surprised at how he made conker sweets. He gave me a packet of conker sweets.

Then I went outside and saw a lion and the lion tried to chase me. I gave it some of the conker sweets and it settled down. I crept away quietly so that I didn't wake him.

I went home to my house in Sweetieland and I made a sweetie pie, it tasted yummy. Then the ten aliens and I had a piece of sweetie pie and it was yummy.

Then I went outside and it was snowing. When it had stopped snowing, I went back outside and made a snowman. I went back inside to get a carrot sweet for his nose. Then we put the carrot sweet on his nose and we had finished making the snowman.

Then we decided to make snow angels. All of us made twenty-five snow angels. When we had finished making snow angels we decided to make a snow wall. When we finished making the snow wall, we went inside and had some tea.

Benjamin Dylan Shelmerdine (6)

Shillington Lower School, Shillington

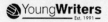

Dear Diary

I went to Disneyland and I saw a mermaid who was called Ariel and of course, I saw Tinkerbell and lots of princesses. I went with Mummy and Daddy and a colourful unicorn. The unicorn was called Flash. While I was there, I had double ice creams and then I went home. It was a very long journey back home. I had to fly on two aeroplanes back home, it hurt my ears on the aeroplane. I was flying back home and I dropped my teddy. I was home by then and saw my teddy on the floor. I quickly picked it up and ran to Mummy and Daddy and my pet unicorn. I saw my house. I went inside and ran upstairs and jumped into my bed and went to sleep.

Summer Olivia Loader (5)
Shillington Lower School, Shillington

Dear Diary

I went to my friend's house and I had tea and biscuits and I had loads of fun. I went to the trampolines and I bought ice cream. I saw a cat, it scratched me and I went home. I found my lost teddy, it was magical but I didn't know the teddy was magical. I loved the magical teddy, it flew me to America. On the way, I found a map. It led me home and I saw lots of magical animals, I wanted to see them all.

I woke up the next day and I saw them again. I was so happy, the animals were blue, purple and pretty. After that, I was so tired out I went back to bed. I dreamt about a princess.

Thea-Mar Greenwood-Mortelmans (6)

Shillington Lower School, Shillington

Dear Diary

I went to Center Parcs today and I swam in the outdoor pool with no hat on my head. I saw a horse with a person on it in a stable. I saw an aeroplane and a unicorn called Sparkle with a sparkly horn. It had a picture on its horn which glowed in the dark like a shooting star but lots of shooting stars. My mummy was watching from beside the pool and my dad was watching too. When I went to Center Parcs, it was summertime and I went into the pool with Kara, my friend and she didn't have a hat on either. The unicorn came with us too and we had a picnic as well.

Martha Burr (6)
Shillington Lower School, Shillington

Dear Diary

Today I went to the beach and I had a chocolate cake with yellow icing on top. It was yummy. I saw a unicorn in a bush and I helped it out of the bush. It was pink. I went for a swim in the water. I also saw a mermaid in a rainbow colour with red hair. I loved it so much. Her tail was red, just like her hair. I wanted to keep it but when I turned around, the mermaid was gone. I was sad. I started crying. I looked in the water and the mermaid was there and I was happy again. The mermaid had red wings. The mermaid came out of the sea. We had a chat together.

Limani Mauger (5)
Shillington Lower School, Shillington

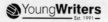

Dear Diary

I went up Everest and it was cold but I wore boots. It was terrifying! I went with my friend Heath. It took nine hours to get up it. We went on motorbikes to get to it. There was a steep path, it was bumpy. It was fun but the weather was dull. It got freezing and then our legs turned numb. We went down on snowboards which was fun. There was a cafe and we went inside. It was hot. In it, we drank Coke and ate chicken. Then we roared home on our motorbikes. It was a thrilling day.

Elliott Alexander Radelat (6)
Shillington Lower School, Shillington

Dear Diary

Today Elliot, Toby and I rode hoverboards to a train track. Then, unfortunately, it started to rain so we hid under a train. Then I got out a pack of sweets from my pocket. Toby got three packets of chocolate frogs out of his pocket and Elliot got a pack of Bertie Bott's: Every Flavour Beans. Toby got a vomit flavour and Elliott got a bogey flavour one. Then it stopped raining, so we got back on our hoverboards and went home.

Dexter Ritchie (6)

Shillington Lower School, Shillington

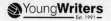

Dear Diary

I went to Disneyland and I went on a train. I saw Elsa and Anna and also my uncles and aunties. I went with my mummy and daddy. I saw Ariel the mermaid and I ate sausages with her. Then I went to the hotel and went in the hotel jacuzzi. My friends and I had lots of fun eating sweets and going on rides. The next day, we went to Ariel's castle in the sea. It was so much fun.

Adora Bella J Cordt (6)
Shillington Lower School, Shillington

Dear Diary

Yesterday I went to Pokémon land with my friend, Raichu. I flew on Raichu and I went into the forest. I caught lots of Pokémon and then it rained really hard. When Raichu was working hard suddenly Raichu evolved into Mega Raichu. His stripes disappeared and he learnt a new move so then we trained hard. The new move was Thunder Shock.

Heath Kidd (5)
Shillington Lower School, Shillington

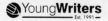

Dear Diary

Yesterday I went to Magical Land and I saw Rosanna from Tinkerbell. I saw a mermaid and her hair was red. I met a unicorn whose name was Cinderella. I ate sweets and I drank a milkshake. I hated to part with my best friends. I had to go home and on the way home, I saw a princess. When I got home, it looked magical.

Lottie Howarth (5)
Shillington Lower School, Shillington

Dear Diary

I flew on a plane and went on a train. Then I got out of the train and had lunch with my mum and then I went to Hamsterland. It was fun. I went to the toyshop and I got Heelys. Then I went home and had dinner. Then I found a crystal on the grass and I played on my iPad.

Chester Baker-Leach (6)
Shillington Lower School, Shillington

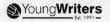

Dear Diary

Today I went to school with my mum. On my way, I ate some sweets. After that, I went to the park and I went on the slide and my friends came to the park. I found a treasure chest full of diamonds and gold. Then I ate some chocolate. I took the treasure chest home.

Teddy Witherspoon (5)
Shillington Lower School, Shillington

Dear Diary

I went inside Dragon Castle. I was going with my nana. I went on my Hydrolixs. It was eight hours to get there. It was dark and there was a giant alpha that was alive. It was ginormous. It had a ginormous head and its tail was 122 metres long!

Leo Rome Scott (6)

Shillington Lower School, Shillington

Dear Diary

Today I went to Popcorn-Ninja Land. I smelled the popcorn and they were chasing me. I ate them, they were yummy. I went with my cat called Cardi and I got there by riding Superman. I wish I could fly there forever and ever and ever.

Phoenix Williams (6)
Shillington Lower School, Shillington

Dear Diary

I went to the park with my mum. She drove the car fast so that I could have more playtime. At the park, I borrowed a scooter to go down the slide on it. I fell off but laughed.

Kai Barrett (5)

Shillington Lower School, Shillington

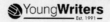

Dear Diary

I went to the beach with a unicorn and we saw a mermaid. I was excited to see her. She had red glossy hair and a glossy blue tail. She was called Ariel.

Elsie Daniel (5)
Shillington Lower School, Shillington

Dear Diary

When I woke up I went downstairs to watch TV. Then I ate breakfast, watched more TV and got dressed. I went to soft play. We were about to go but we saw my friend playing football so I started playing. It was kids vs adults. My dad got my sister and they both joined in.

After that I went to Simon's. I had doorstep toast with sausages. I loved it.

I went home and watched a movie. We went upstairs and fell asleep.

Next morning it was super Sunday. I ate breakfast, it was yummy. I got dressed then went to soft play with my sister. After that I played football. It was lovely. The score was 7-0. It was the best time ever.

Bob O'Byrne Kehoe (7)

St Bernadette Catholic Primary School, London Colney

Dear Diary

On Sunday me and my friends Oliver, Dora and Lenard were getting ready for the big trip to Heartwood Forest. At lunchtime we all got in the car and waited for my mummy to come to the big blue car. When we arrived we had to park the car. After my mummy parked the car we went into the small forest. Not long after, we found the magical place where you could make houses out of sticks.

Soon we finished ours and it was time to go home, but before we all went home we had a little picnic that made me feel very happy because I was hungry.

My favourite part of the day was when we made a house. It was the best day ever.

Anikó Coyne (7)

St Bernadette Catholic Primary School, London Colney

Dear Diary

On Saturday I went to do a litter pick with Beavers. We cleaned the whole London Colney.

After that I went home very tired. I had pizza for lunch. At the litter pick lots of people said, "Well done," so I went home proud.

My best part of the day was doing good work even though it was tiring.

On Sunday I was with my family. We went to church and had fun.

After that we went to the park with our scooters. We went round the park. When we had finished we went to the play area.

I loved when we went on the scooters. I had the best weekend ever!

Alistair Nathan Hanna (7)

St Bernadette Catholic Primary School, London Colney

Dear Diary

I went to the cinema. I watched The Kid Who Would Be King. The character found a huge grey sword. It was amazing. I watched it with my nanny and my brother.

At lunchtime I had McDonald's. I had a burger.

After we went to my nanny's house and played with Dylan the dog, he bit me a lot but he is only a puppy. He is really fluffy. We watched Shrek.

I had dinner with Nanny, it was a roast chicken.

Then my mum picked me up and took me home.

My favourite bit of my day was the movie!

Noah Howard (6)

St Bernadette Catholic Primary School, London Colney

Dear Diary

Yesterday I went to the funfair. I needed to get a ticket to get in. First I bought some candy. After that I went on a ride and I saw a beautiful door. I pushed the door open and no one was there. I looked around and I saw an amazing treasure. Then I saw a mermaid, she was very beautiful and I heard my unicorn calling me. Before I knew it I was gone for lunch. Finally I went on a roller coaster, that was my favourite bit. It was the best time of my life.

Holly Vanderhoven (7)

St Bernadette Catholic Primary School, London Colney

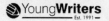

Dear Diary

On Saturday I went to a Chinese restaurant called Bang Bang. After going to the restaurant with my dad we went to the play area in Stevenage. When we left the play area we drove to Tesco and saw my mum. At home me and my family had dinner. Then I changed into my pyjamas then I went to bed. On Sunday I stayed at home and did my homework. After that I played with slime. Then me and my family had dinner. Then I changed into my pyjamas and went to bed.

Megan De Sa Fernandes (7)

St Bernadette Catholic Primary School, London Colney

Dear Diary

On Saturday morning I woke up to eat my breakfast. My mum wanted us to go to McDonald's. I went with my family. We went to the car. When we arrived we ate chips, orange juice, Coca-Cola and burgers. My mum and dad ate delicious pie.

After that, me and my big sister and my little sister got Lego Movie 2 keyrings. I was so full of joy at McDonald's!

My favourite part of the day was getting the Lego Movie 2 keyrings.

Chigozirim Okoh (7)

St Bernadette Catholic Primary School, London Colney

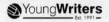
Dear Diary

On Saturday me and my brother went to football. I watched my brother play football. Then my strong friends came. Then we all went in. After that I went to my grandad's. Yesterday I went to my nanny and grandad's. First we went in then my auntie and my cousin and my little cousins came too. We all went outside. We played football.
I had an amazing, exciting weekend!

Maxwell Gatta (6)
St Bernadette Catholic Primary School, London Colney

Dear Diary

Yesterday I went to Spain, I had Spanish food. Then I went with a unicorn so I asked it, "Can I have a ride?"

It was so fun.

Then I saw a mermaid.

After lunch suddenly a big silvery snake bit me. Then I hurt my head. Then I saw treasure!

My favourite part of the day was when I saw treasure.

Sienna Enstone (6)

St Bernadette Catholic Primary School, London Colney

Dear Diary

You would not believe the amazing week I have had! Last week, I went on a road trip with my kind family and my loud, black puppy called Indy. We drove past a sign that said *Fairyland*. My mum didn't believe it was real, so I went in. Fairyland was so colourful. I met a fairy called Lavender and she had a purple leaf dress, pink shoes with a flower on top and wavy brown hair. First, we went fishing for fish which were as shiny as sequins. I felt amazing! Next, we felt hungry so we went to Butterbean's cafe. We had tasty chips with ketchup. We were tired after all of that, so we went to bed and squeezed our toys.

Emily Sproule (7)
Windermere Primary School, St Albans

Dear Diary

I had the most amazing weekend ever. I went to the special cinema in a taxi with Mow, the fluffy, orange monster. Unfortunately, our huge movie screen was not ready and Mow remembered that we had no salt and toffee popcorn. We got some salt and toffee popcorn from the popcorn vending machine. By midnight, I felt very worried because it was late. I finally watched Captain Marvel which we all wanted to watch.

I came home and I climbed up to my tree house. I said goodbye to Mow and he went. I wrote a birthday card because it will be Mow's birthday party tomorrow. I drew a puppy too. Now I am writing in the light of the moon.

Ilia Bruce (7)

Windermere Primary School, St Albans

Dear Diary

You will not believe the amazing day I had yesterday. I woke up and got dressed, then I went downstairs to the car. We were going to a magical zoo.

When we got there, I went to the playroom for ten minutes. Then I heard an alarm so I grabbed the emergency key and put in in the emergency key hole. We were safe until, *bang!* All the animals were destroyed. I got people to safety because I was the oldest. Then the security asked me to be a guard and I said I would be. I rode a donkey home.

Idris Hylton (7)
Windermere Primary School, St Albans

Dear Diary

Do you want to hear about the day I've had? I went to the caravan with my family and my pet, Bunny. We had to go to the shop because we had run out of bunny food. I left the door open and I lost Bunny! Then I had an idea. I dropped bunny food all over the caravan and I found Bunny! I felt so happy and we saw an ice cream van, so I asked my mummy so nicely. We got it and I had chocolate ice cream. When we were going home, I had to drop Bunny's food so that Bunny could follow me.

Rose Fitzgerald (7)
Windermere Primary School, St Albans

Dear Diary

You would not believe the day I've had. Earlier this morning, I went to the attic because my mum told me I needed to clean the attic. I found a precious map, so I cleaned the attic and followed the precious map. Can you guess what I found? It was a mythical mission. I went inside and found a slimy monster guarding infinite gold. I found a room full of guns and then I found a minigun and killed the monster. Then I was rich and got more gold. Finally, I went home and I felt great!

Efehan Gok (6)
Windermere Primary School, St Albans

Dear Diary

I had a very fun day at the hot, sandy desert. I decided to take a walk with Floppy, my dog when ten puppies came along chasing us. Then I knew why they were chasing us, they needed Floppy and me to find their mummy dog. I saw something next to the waterfall and I ran to it and the puppies followed me. I had found her, she was drinking some water. When she saw her puppies, she was jumping around. It was time for Floppy and me to go home, so I hugged the puppies and went back home.

Sivani M Nair (6)
Windermere Primary School, St Albans

Dear Diary

You would not believe the day I've had. We were having a small walk with my family. We followed the footsteps when we got there and my family and I fell into quicksand. Then a superhero helped us and the superhero looked like he had a yellow and red suit and a black cape. Then a gingerbread man appeared and I ate him. I was very happy to see the superhero because I had never seen a superhero before. I knew he was going to save us because he looked very big and kind.

Safwan (7)
Windermere Primary School, St Albans

Dear Diary

You would not believe the day I've had.
Early this morning, I went downstairs and
my mum told me there was a pot of gold
and a crown in a castle near my home. I
went with my mum. I went into the creaky
castle but then a witch appeared. I tried to
fight and I found a pot of ink and I poured it
all over the witch's face and I ran all the
way home. I felt terrified.
My mum and I watched a film at home on
the TV. I had such an adventure; I loved it.

Scarlett Campbell (6)

Windermere Primary School, St Albans

Dear Diary

You would not believe the awesome day I've had, I woke up and walked out of my house in Cave Land. Then I found a huge castle ruin and inside the ruin, there were gross, slouching zombies. As soon as they could, they threw me into a dark and gloomy dungeon. A few minutes later, I used my belt to make a key and escaped. I ran to the next room and in there, I found a chest. I felt so happy. I jumped into the chest and took a sword out and ran all the way home.

Josh Treanor (7)
Windermere Primary School, St Albans

Dear Diary

You would not believe the day I've had. Yesterday, I went to the football stadium with my dad. While we were there, my dad and I saw Harry Kane and he was playing football against Arsenal. It was 1-0 in the first half. Then Tottenham scored again. Then Arsenal scored a goal. Finally, full time was way up and it was 2-7 and Tottenham had won the game. I was so happy that Tottenham had won. Then I went home with my dad.

Tomos Hughes (7)

Windermere Primary School, St Albans

Dear Diary

You would not believe your eyes! A few days ago, I was walking in the forest, going to meet my friend Sammy, the happy elf. Suddenly, it started raining and I got lost. The rain came down heavier and heavier, so I hid under a leaf. Then I waited for hours and hours. Eventually, the rain stopped and the sun came out! I could fly again! I felt lonely but then I flew back home. A fairy's life is very exhausting!

Mackenzie Stokes Boucher (7)
Windermere Primary School, St Albans

Dear Diary

You would not believe the day I had yesterday. I woke up in the early morning and went down the stairs. Then I opened the door and went for a walk with my sister Marlie. While we were walking, we saw some yummy looking sweets and so we ate them. We still felt hungry and we saw a gingerbread man so we ate him too. After that, we found an ice cream tree and we ate lots of ice cream. Then I got a tummy ache.

Darcie Bayliss (7)
Windermere Primary School, St Albans

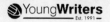

Dear Diary

You would not believe the exciting day I've had! I was at home playing Minecraft when something weird happened. Everything was blocky. I was *in* Minecraft, I was in front of a portal! I went to the random, flickering portal. Stegy and Stegy's toy clung to me extremely tightly. It hurt and we spotted dinosaurs. I was so shocked that I fainted and woke up. Then I ran into the portal.

Luke Winston Chapman (6)
Windermere Primary School, St Albans

Dear Diary

You would not believe the day I've had! I went into a rainforest and made a special friend, a unicorn, and its name was Cupcake. Then I saw a rainbow and I walked more and more until I got to the end of the rainbow. I stopped because I didn't know what to do. Suddenly, I found a golden egg. The chicken looked like it would come out but I thought it might not come out. Then it did.

Nailah Rahman (7)

Windermere Primary School, St Albans

Dear Diary

You would not believe the amazing night I've had. During the night, in my new house, I woke up and explored my new house. First I went to the attic. There I found a portal so I jumped into the portal and then I was in Candy Land. After that, I picked some sweets.

Finally, I came back from the portal. I felt delighted. In the end, I carried all the sweets and ate them all.

Jayden De La Cruz (6)

Windermere Primary School, St Albans

Dear Diary

You would not believe the day I've had. I went to the beach alone. The sun was very hot and I was very thirsty. I noticed a buzzard and then I noticed more buzzards too. Oh no! They were circling me. Luckily I found a shop. I bought some water and then I ran away. I was so happy to get away from the birds. Finally, I went home to watch TV. It was a documentary about birds.

Jake Lawrence Bishop (6)
Windermere Primary School, St Albans

Dear Diary

You would not believe the day I've had. Earlier this morning, I went to a mysterious forest because my cat had run away. On the way to find my cat, I came across an enchanted castle. I went inside it and I saw a bloodthirsty bat. It began to chase me and I got scared. Then I saw my cat. I grabbed my cat and ran away. I will never go back there again.

Sophie Anne-Marie Hubbard (7)
Windermere Primary School, St Albans

Dear Diary

You would not believe the day I had yesterday, I went to the football stadium and I found Luka Modric playing football. It was good, I was really hoping that Modric would give me a gold ball.

This morning, it's my birthday and Dad gave me a gold World Cup. I ate my cake and it was really good. My friends came and I was happy.

Natanael Musija (7)

Windermere Primary School, St Albans

Dear Diary

You won't believe the day I've had, I was waiting for my mum in the car with my nice dad because she was getting contacts. I saw a poor person on the streets. Then I felt bad for him because he only had 6p. Then I gave him a shiny 2p and he had 8p altogether. Then I felt good. I went back to the car and I went home jubilant.

Hamzah Zaman (7)
Windermere Primary School, St Albans

Dear Diary

You would not believe the day I've had. Early this morning, I woke up and noticed I was in Dinosaur Land. A bloodthirsty dinosaur appeared out of the gloom. After that, a lot more came and they were destroying the town. Just then, dragons saved the day. I was shocked but the good news was, that there was a happy ending!

Sol Cedillo-Cohen (7)

Windermere Primary School, St Albans

Dear Diary

You will not believe the day I've had! We went swimming in the Pacific Ocean and I found a cute sea serpent. The sea serpent liked me. Then, I happily rode it but suddenly grey sharks attacked. Soon the sea serpent ate the greedy sharks and I felt amazed. Later on, the sea serpent took me home.

Ronin Marshall (7)
Windermere Primary School, St Albans

Dear Diary

Yesterday I had ice cream in the hotel with my family. We were on holiday. I noticed sweets on the floor, so I picked them up and followed them. Next, I saw a unicorn with a golden horn. After that, I felt amazed because I had never seen a unicorn before. The unicorn followed me everywhere.

Taryn Marima (7)

Windermere Primary School, St Albans

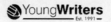

Dear Diary

On Wednesday, I went on a school trip to the Natural History Museum but before that, I got my bag ready, then I went to the museum on a coach.

When I got there, I saw a gigantic dinosaur skeleton, then I went to a big room. I saw some more dinosaur skeletons.

After the dinosaur skeletons, we went to the insect bit. We saw some butterflies, daddy longlegs, we saw lots of insects. I went into a big hole and I saw lots of animals in the window. I saw bears and even polar bears! I saw lots of different animals, then I went to have lunch. I had a good lunch.

After lunch, I went on the escalator and we saw our planet. Then I saw an earthquake. I went into a big room and saw the big whale. I saw the giraffe skeleton, then I got into the coach.

Iaryna Andreea Tase (7)
Yewtree Primary School, Hemel Hempstead

Dear Diary

Today we went to the Natural History Museum. I thought it would be boring. We went in a coach. Me and Freya decided to talk about our day.

When we arrived, we saw a sign that said: *Whale Hello There!* It made me giggle. When we went inside, it looked exciting. We saw a red Earth. I was scared to go in! We saw some weird, creepy skulls, then we found the creepy-crawlies. We saw a house, it had a lot of bugs! Then we had a scrumptious lunch. I had some soft sandwiches and angel slices.

After lunch, we all saw a robot dinosaur! Then we saw a gigantic whale, it was huge! It was time to go back on the coach. We slept like the animals on our way back to school.

Alyssa Steeden (7)
Yewtree Primary School, Hemel Hempstead

Dear Diary

Yesterday we went to the Natural History Museum in London. We went on a coach first, some of us sang songs and slept.
We arrived. It was built in 1920. It's definitely ancient!
After that, we went inside. The first thing I saw was a meteorite, a giant one! We went inside, it was all orange!
In the red zone we saw a volcano, it was scary. There was a moving floor.
In the green zone, the first thing I wanted to see was the creepy-crawlies.
In the blue zone, we learnt that the bowhead whale is 3,000 metres long. That's the size of 1,000 buses, and 300 metres wide!
Did you know male seahorses get pregnant?

Lukas Rodière Davis (7)
Yewtree Primary School, Hemel Hempstead

Dear Diary

Today I went on a beautiful, colourful coach to the Natural History Museum in London. After a while, I got to the museum. I reached up to the cool doors and saw hundreds of people. I thought I would get lost but I didn't. I saw the huge whale over my small head. I was in Miss Backhouse's group. We saw lots of dinosaurs, I was amazed because a dinosaur head was on top of Miss Backhouse's head! I told her to look on top of her head. She looked, she saw it. She said, "A dinosaur head, I like it!" Amazing.

Finally, I saw the earthquake. The floor started moving and shaking from side to side!

Hafza Khan (6)

Yewtree Primary School, Hemel Hempstead

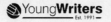

Dear Diary

On Wednesday, I went to the Natural History Museum for a school trip. First we went on a coach to London, it took a long time, but when I got there, I saw a dinosaur! It was huge and massive.

Next, I saw a giraffe. It was long. I saw a big tree and a big polar bear, it was white and had a big neck.

When I went to the creepy-crawly house, it had a spider in it. It had long legs.

I went to see the big whale, then I went to see a little dinosaur. I went to see the earthquakes in the shop, it was shaking! It was not scary at all. Then we saw a big dolphin and that was my day! I went back to school.

Maisie Puddephatt (7)
Yewtree Primary School, Hemel Hempstead

Dear Diary

On Wednesday, Year 2B and 2S went to the
Natural History Museum. We travelled there
by coach, it was exciting. We were all taking
pictures with the dinosaur at the entrance.
After that, we all split up in our groups. My
group went to the escalator. We went down
the stairs, we saw the big whale in the
colossal hall.
Next, we went to the dinosaur part, then we
went to the insect room.
After, we met up in the hall and had lunch.
After lunch, we looked at the animals. We
went downstairs and upstairs. We went to
look at the insects again.
Finally, we met back up to go home.

Oscar Harris (7)
Yewtree Primary School, Hemel Hempstead

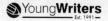

Dear Diary

Yesterday we went on a coach to the Natural History Museum. I sat with my partner, Jayden, I felt so excited!
After an hour, we arrived. When we went in, I saw a big, scary triceratops. There were millions of people. Then we saw an electric dinosaur. It was frightening.
We went to the red zones. After that, we went through an earthquake, then we went to see some space stuff. There was so much! Then we went to have some lunch.
After, we went to the blue zone and we saw the humpback whale and a skeleton. It was gigantic and enormous!
Then we went home, we were late!

Mason Stephen William Lane (7)
Yewtree Primary School, Hemel Hempstead

Dear Diary

On Wednesday, I went on a school trip to the Natural History Museum. I saw dinosaur bones and had fun. I saw a whale and then I went for lunch.

When I was done, I went to my group and we went to the wildlife garden. I followed them and they took me to a scorpion! It moved its tail and its pincers, that scared me!

We saw a big, long whale, it was really great. Then we saw a rhino with a horn. We got back on the coach. I was tired so I fell asleep on the way back to school. It was a great day.

Marley-Jay Daniel O'Hara (6)

Yewtree Primary School, Hemel Hempstead

Dear Diary

On Wednesday, we went to the Natural History Museum in London. First we got on the coach to travel there. I sat with my partner. I heard singing so I started to sing as well.

When we got there, I was excited. We split up into groups. The part with the electronic T-rex was my favourite, it was huge and it roared loudly. Some people were crying! We went upstairs, then we ate lunch. Then we went to see some mammals. I saw an orca on a huge wall, it was the size of a giant!

Saif Akthar (6)
Yewtree Primary School, Hemel Hempstead

Dear Diary

On Wednesday, we all went to the big Natural History Museum in London. First we all needed to get on a big coach.

On the coach, me and Macy were telling jokes to each other, then the coach started to move.

After a while, we arrived in London and we all took a picture together in the museum. Next, we all split into our groups. We saw a stuffed bunny. We got to stroke it, it was so fluffy. It was so brown but its feet were tied up with a strap and a nail!

Lola Rose Taylor (6)

Yewtree Primary School, Hemel Hempstead

Dear Diary

Yesterday we went on a school trip to learn about dinosaur bones. We saw the big blue whale. We went to see the dinosaur eggs. We went to see the models and the wild garden. In there, we went on a hunt and it was fun. We went to go to meet up with everybody else to have lunch.

After lunch, we went to see the birds, then we got back onto the coach. Now I will tell you where we went for our school trip... The Natural History Museum!

Safa Akhtar (6)

Yewtree Primary School, Hemel Hempstead

Dear Diary

On Wednesday, we went on a coach and arrived at the Natural History Museum. We went up a long escalator. I nearly fell down! We saw a giant blue whale, then we saw a moving scorpion! We had lunch.

After lunch, we saw a moving dinosaur. It was so scary, I didn't want to see it ever again in my life!

We saw a dodo bird and an ostrich. We went on a scavenger hunt, then we saw a polar bear.

We went home on the coach.

Leo Atticus Trinder (6)

Yewtree Primary School, Hemel Hempstead

Dear Diary

On Wednesday, I went on a school trip to the Natural History Museum. I went on a coach. It took an hour, then we went in. We had a picture taken, then I went to see the birds. We saw a huge whale, a moving town and a dinosaur!
Later, we had lunch, then I went on an escalator. I went into a shaking room! We saw a bit of a tree.
Later, we went to the coach. I fell asleep. Then we went back to school. I loved it.

Sienna Wright (7)

Yewtree Primary School, Hemel Hempstead

Dear Diary

On Wednesday, I went on a school trip to the Natural History Museum.
When we got there, I saw lots of birds. I liked the penguins the best. Then we went to the dinosaur. It could move and roar. Then we went to see some animals. I saw a lion, it was very scary. I saw a big polar bear, an elephant, a blue whale and creepy-crawlies. There were bugs everywhere!
Then we got on the coach and went back to school.

Courtney Lawson (6)

Yewtree Primary School, Hemel Hempstead

Dear Diary

Yesterday I went on a school trip to the Natural History Museum. I went to see the gross bones and then I went to see the big blue whale, it was huge! I went to see the bugs, then I went for lunch.
After, I went to see the big polar bear, I loved it! Then I went to see the animatronic dinosaurs, then I saw the lovely volcano.
I went back to the coach, went back to school and went home.

Hira Khan (6)

Yewtree Primary School, Hemel Hempstead

Dear Diary

On Wednesday, we went to the Natural History Museum on the adorable bus. We saw Toys 'R' Us and then we arrived at the museum and saw a robotic T-rex, the king of the dinosaurs! We went to see the colossal whale, there were six whales. Then we went into a big meteor and went up a ramp and the ground started shaking crazily!
Finally, we saw the creepy-crawly house.

Reece Keenan (6)
Yewtree Primary School, Hemel Hempstead

Dear Diary

On Wednesday, I went on a school trip to the Natural History Museum. I saw a dinosaur bone, then we went to look at earthquakes and we went into the shop simulator. We went to look at the big blue whale, it was massive! Then we went to the wildlife garden and looked for bugs. We saw ants, slugs and ladybirds.
After that, we got back in the coach and went to school.

Cameron Thackeray (7)
Yewtree Primary School, Hemel Hempstead

Dear Diary

On Wednesday, we went to the Natural History Museum in London. First we got on a coach to get there. I sat with my partner and went to sleep.

After a while, we arrived at the museum. We saw a whale, a triceratops, lots of birds and lots of dinos.

We went on an escalator to see an earthquake as well as a robot dino and a T-rex robot dino.

Ollie Newton-Smith (6)

Yewtree Primary School, Hemel Hempstead

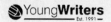

Dear Diary

On Wednesday, we went to the Natural History Museum in London. First we all had to get on a coach to go to the museum. I sat with my partner and we sang all the way.
Next, we investigated the dinosaur save. We saw a colossal, grey dinosaur!
Finally, we saw magnificent birds.

Dylan Thomas McLaughlin (6)
Yewtree Primary School, Hemel Hempstead

Dear Diary

Yesterday we went to the museum to see lots of old things.
First we got on the coach to London. Me and Alyssa decided to play with our toys. Soon, we arrived in London. Then we went to see some dinosaurs!

Freya Burch (7)
Yewtree Primary School, Hemel Hempstead

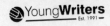

Dear Diary

Yesterday I went on a school trip to London to the Natural History Museum.
At first, I saw earthquakes and volcanoes. Then I saw a polar bear. I saw the big blue whale and then the scorpion!

Riley Solomon (7)
Yewtree Primary School, Hemel Hempstead

YoungWriters
— Est. 1991 —

Young Writers Information

We hope you have enjoyed reading this book – and that you will continue to in the coming years.

If you're a young writer who enjoys reading and creative writing, or the parent of an enthusiastic poet or story writer, do visit our website **www.youngwriters.co.uk**. Here you will find free competitions, workshops and games, as well as recommended reads, a poetry glossary and our blog. There's lots to keep budding writers motivated to write!

If you would like to order further copies of this book, or any of our other titles, then please give us a call or order via your online account.

Young Writers
Remus House
Coltsfoot Drive
Peterborough
PE2 9BF
(01733) 890066
info@youngwriters.co.uk

Join in the conversation!
Tips, news, giveaways and much more!

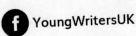 YoungWritersUK   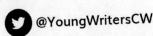 @YoungWritersCW